BANANAS IN PYJAMAS

BANANAS IN PYJAMAS

PRESENT

Written by Brenda Apsley and Vicki Adams
Edited by Nina Filipek
Designed and Illustrated by Geoff Ball

Copyright © Australian Broadcasting Corporation 1996
All rights reserved. Published in Great Britain in 1996 by
World International Limited, Deanway Technology Centre,
Wilmslow Road, Handforth, Cheshire SK9 3FB.
Printed in Great Britain. ISBN 0 7498 2812 9

Hello from

Rat in a Hat

B1

B2

Lulu   Morgan   Amy

Welcome to Cuddles Avenue

This is where B1, B2 and the Teddies live.
Look at the picture, then answer the questions.

6

1. Who is waving from the windows?
2. Where is Lulu?
3. Who is clearing up leaves?
4. Who is knocking on the Bananas' front door?

The answers are on page 61

7

Munchy Honey Cakes Time!

The Bananas were hungry. "Are you thinking what I'm thinking, B1?" asked B2. "I think, I am, B2," said B1. "It's Munchy Honey Cakes Time!"

B1 and B2 thought about eating yummy Munchy Honey Cakes. The Bananas kept them in a big biscuit tin in the kitchen.

The Bananas opened the tin where they kept the Munchy Honey Cakes. "Oh, no, B1!" "Oh, no, B2! There are no more Munchy Honey Cakes left!"

"Never mind," said B2. "We can make some more." He opened the big cook book and turned to the Munchy Honey Cakes recipe.

As B1 read out the recipe B2 put the ingredients on the worktop. "You read out what we need and I'll collect everything," said B2.

B1 took out a big bowl. "Five cups of cornflakes," B1 read out. B2 counted the cups. "One, two, three, four..." he said. Then he stopped.

B2 got mixed up. He couldn't remember how many cups of cornflakes he had put into the bowl. Was it four cups, or was it five?

Next B1 read out, "One cup of honey, B2." B2 picked up the big jar of honey and poured some into the bowl. It was runny and sticky.

B2 stirred the honey into the cornflakes. He used a big wooden spoon. "That looks good fun, B2," said B1. "Can I try stirring?" B2 gave him the spoon.

"What goes in next?" asked B1. B2 read out the recipe. "One cup of honey," he said, and poured more honey into the bowl. "We just did that!" said B1.

B2 put ten cups of coconut into the bowl. "Anything else, B2?" said B1. B2 looked in the book. "We need butter, sultanas and sunflower seed kernels."

"You have a turn at reading, B1," said B2. "I'll do the mixing." The recipe said one cup of sultanas, but B1 thought it said ten! The bowl was VERY full.

10

B2 stirred and stirred and stirred.
It was hard work. Then he put spoonfuls of
the mixture into bun cases. There was a lot
of mixture left over.

The Bananas put the Munchy Honey Cakes
in the fridge. But they couldn't wait to try
them, and took them out before they were
set.

Oh, dear. The cakes were still just a messy
mixture. The Bananas were thinking the
same thing. "Yeuk!" said B1. "Yeuk!" said
B2.

"Are you thinking what I'm thinking, B1?"
"I think I am, B2," said B1. "It's Cookery
Lesson Time! Let's go and find Morgan!"
And that is what they did!

Munchy Honey Cakes to Make

"I'm going to show the Bananas how to make REAL Munchy Honey Cakes. Why don't you make some too?"

Before you begin...

* Ask a grown-up to help you.

* Wash your hands.

* Collect everything you need.

You will need:

100g butter

$\frac{3}{4}$ cup clear honey

$\frac{1}{2}$ cup sunflower seed kernels

5 cups cornflakes

$\frac{1}{2}$ cup desiccated coconut

50g sultanas

1. Ask a grown-up to melt the butter and honey in a saucepan. Boil the mixture for 5 minutes.

2. Put the cornflakes in a big bowl. Crush them with a spoon. Mix in the sunflower seeds, sultanas and coconut.

3. Pour the butter and honey on to the dry things. Mix them together well.

4. Put 1 tablespoon of mixture into each cup of a bun tin or paper bun case.

5. Put the cakes in the fridge until they are set (hard).

Lulu's Lessons

Lulu loves ballet dancing. One day she decided to make up a brand new dance.

She first twirled on one foot and then the other. She walked high on her tippy toes then took a bow. But she couldn't think what to do next.

"Maybe Morgan will help me with my new dance. He always has lots of clever ideas." So Lulu went to find Morgan.

Morgan was very busy painting a rocket ship he had just made.

"Hello, Morgan," said Lulu. "I came to ask you for some help. I'm making up a brand new ballet dance but I need some more steps."

But Morgan needed to finish painting his rocket before the paint dried and suggested that Lulu should ask Amy for some ideas. So Lulu went to find Amy.

Lulu found Amy planting some large yellow daisies.

"Hello, Amy," said Lulu. "Will you look at my new dance? It's too short and I thought you could help me make up some more steps."

But Amy hadn't finished planting her daisies and suggested that Lulu should find the Bananas in Pyjamas to see if they could help.

So Lulu went to the beach to find the Bananas.

B1 and B2 were on Beach Patrol. "Hello, Lulu," said the Bananas.

"Hello, Bananas," said Lulu. "I need some more steps for my new dance."

But the Bananas hadn't finished cleaning the beach. "Sorry, Lulu," said the Bananas. "Perhaps we could help you later."

Lulu looked very sad. "No one will help me with my new dance. If only there was a ballet school in Cuddles Avenue."

That gave the Bananas in Pyjamas a good idea. "Are you thinking what I'm thinking, B1?"

"I think I am, B2."

"It's Helping Time!"

Later that day when Lulu was on her way to Rat in a Hat's shop she was surprised to see a notice that said,

THE CUDDLES AVENUE BALLET SCHOOL

THIS WAY ⟶

Lulu was very excited as she followed the arrows to the Ballet School. Two very tall ballet teachers wearing dark glasses and hats welcomed her.

"This is Ballet Teacher One," said B2.

"And this is Ballet Teacher Two," said B1.

Lulu told them she needed some new steps for her dance. "We will show you some very special new steps," said Ballet Teacher One.

"Very, very special," said Ballet Teacher Two.

The ballet teachers started to dance. One went this way and one went that way. Bump! They bumped into each other and fell to the floor.

Lulu thought it was a very odd step.

16

"Can you show me one more step?" asked Lulu.

The teachers turned round and round, faster and faster. They went so fast that they became very dizzy and had to sit down. Lulu had never seen a step like that.

"Could you show me one more step?" she asked.

This time the teachers twirled so fast that their glasses and their hats came off.

"It's the Bananas in Pyjamas," laughed Lulu. "You trickers!" The Bananas laughed too.

That night Morgan, Amy and Rat in a Hat attended a very special concert given by the pupils and teachers of the Cuddles Avenue Ballet School. Lulu danced her twirls, walked high on her tippy toes and then took a bow. Then she joined the Bananas in Pyjamas in the special new steps. Everyone thought it was the funniest dance they had ever seen and agreed that the Cuddles Avenue Ballet School concert was a great success.

17

Lulu's Puzzle

Lulu wears a tutu when she is ballet dancing. She has lots of other clothes. Here are some of them.

Draw a red circle around the clothes Lulu wears in hot weather.
Draw a blue circle around the clothes Lulu wears in cold weather.
Draw a green circle around the clothes Lulu wears in the rain.

The answers are on page 61

Amy's Alphabet

Can you find the missing letter in each word?
Amy's building blocks will help you.

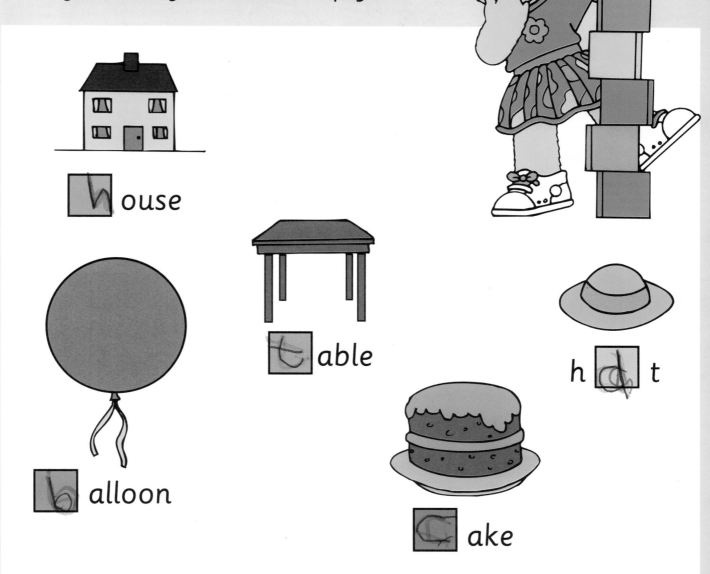

house

table

balloon

cake

h a t

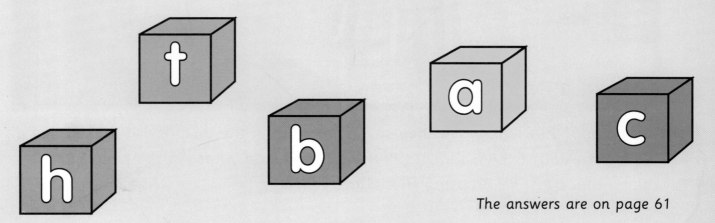

The answers are on page 61

19

Treasure Ahoy!

The Bananas in Pyjamas were on Beach Patrol. "It's a very nice day, B1!" said B2. "A very, very nice day, B2," B1 agreed. As they walked along the beach B1 picked up litter and B2 collected driftwood.

They stopped to look when they saw something in the distance. It looked like a big chest. A big TREASURE chest! "Are you thinking what I'm thinking, B2?" "I think I am, B1." "It's Treasure Hunt Time!"

The Bananas went home and collected the things they needed. They made pirate hats and eye patches. "Ahoy, me Banana matey!" said B2. "Let's go and find the treasure!"

On their way back to the beach the Bananas saw Amy digging in the garden. "Hello, Bananas!" said Amy. "What are you doing?" "We're Pirate Bananas, looking for treasure!" the Bananas replied. "That sounds like fun. Can I come too?" asked Amy. "Of course you can," said the Bananas. So the Bananas and Amy set off to find the treasure.

"Hello!" said Lulu. "Where are you all going?" "On a treasure hunt!" said the Pirate Bananas. "Can I come too?" asked Lulu. "I've never been on a treasure hunt." "Of course you can," said the Bananas. The Bananas, Amy and Lulu set off to find the treasure.

"What an adventure!" said Lulu.
"A proper adventure!" said Amy.
"A treasure adventure!" said B1 and B2.

"I wonder what we will find?" said Amy. "I hope it's lots of golden jelly."
"It might be pearls and jewels," said Lulu. "I could sew them on to my tutu."
"It might be Munchy Honey Cakes!" said B1. "Lots and lots of them!" said B2.

"Hello, everyone!" said Morgan. "What do you think of my treasure chest
sandcastle?" The Pirate Bananas looked disappointed. "Oh no!" cried B1.
"It's not real treasure after all!" "Never mind," said Lulu. "Let's all build
sandcastles." So they did!

Teddy Bear Chase

It's Tuesday, Teddy Bear Chase Day! Play the game with a friend. You can be Amy and Morgan, or B1 and B2. You need a counter each, and a dice. Take turns to throw the dice.
If you throw a 3, move your counter 3 spaces, and so on.

* If you land on a flower, have an extra throw.
* If you land on a stone, miss a turn.
The first player to reach Lulu wins the jelly!

24

I Spy...

There are lots of things in Rat in a Hat's shop. How many can you see that begin with **b**? Say, "I spy with my ratty eye, something begining with **b**!" Can you find 10?

MATHS

COOKBOOK

The answers are on page 61.

Lots of Dots

What are B1 and B2 building? Join the dots to find out.
Colour the picture.

27

Tricky Bananas

The Bananas have played a trick on you. They have made up a story, but there are no words!
Look at the pictures and tell the story.

Hide-and-Seek

B1 and B2 are hiding from Amy and Morgan. "Bananas! Where are you?" call the Teddies. The Bananas aren't saying! They have found very good hiding places! Can you help the Teddies find them?

The answers are on page 61.

29

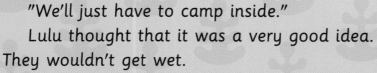

Camping!

Lulu, Amy and Morgan were packed and ready to go. They had their sleeping bags and their torches and lots of food. The Teddies were going camping.

"This will be a great adventure!" said Amy.

"We might not be able to go!" said Lulu. "Look, it's raining!"

"It doesn't matter," said Morgan.

"We'll just have to camp inside."

Lulu thought that it was a very good idea. They wouldn't get wet.

"I'll put up the tent," said Amy helpfully.

Putting up the tent inside was not easy. Morgan and Lulu helped but it kept falling down. Lulu had an idea. She went away and came back with a big sheet and a clothes-horse.

"Let's make a tent in here," she said.

30

Lulu put the clothes-horse up and hung the sheet over it. They all agreed that it made a great tent. The Teddies put their sleeping bags in the tent and climbed inside.

"It should be dark," said Morgan. "We could use our torches."

"I'll switch off the light," said Lulu.

Then the Teddies switched on their torches and played shadows on the walls. They made shapes of birds and rabbits and even the shape of a Munchy Honey Cake.

"I'm hungry," said Amy.

"Let's have our Munchy Honey Cakes," said Lulu.

"This is great!" said Amy. "I love camping."

"We should have asked the Bananas in Pyjamas to come camping with us," said Morgan.

The Teddies didn't know that the Bananas in Pyjamas were peeping through the window!

"What do you think the Teddies are doing?" asked B1. "They've got torches and sleeping bags."

"Maybe they're camping," said B2.

"Are you thinking what I'm thinking, B2?"

"I think I am, B1. It's Trick Time!"

31

The Bananas in Pyjamas decided to be scary monsters and crept home to make their scary monster disguises. While the Bananas were away the Teddies had snuggled down into their sleeping bags and switched off their torches. But just as they were about to go to sleep they heard a strange noise: Oooooo! Ohhhhh ... Oooooo! "What's that?" asked Amy.

"It's nothing," said Lulu. "Go to sleep."

Ooooooohhhhhh! "That doesn't sound like nothing to me," said Morgan. "It sounds like, like a ... scary monster!"

"Don't be silly!" said Lulu.

"I don't believe in scary monsters," said Morgan.

"There's one way to find out," said Amy as she climbed out of her sleeping bag. Lulu and Morgan followed Amy as she quietly opened the door and crept outside.

Then they heard the noise again.

"That doesn't sound like a scary monster," said Amy.

Morgan quickly switched on the torch. "No," he said. "That sounds like scary Bananas!"

"Wearing white sheets over their blue and white striped pyjamas!" said Lulu.

"You trickers!" cried Amy.

"Go and get your sleeping bags, Bananas," said Lulu. "Come camping with us! It's fun, as long as there are no scary monsters around!"

Indoor Camping!

Make an indoor tent using a table and some sheets or blankets or you could use a big cardboard box. Lie it on its side and use the flaps as doors.

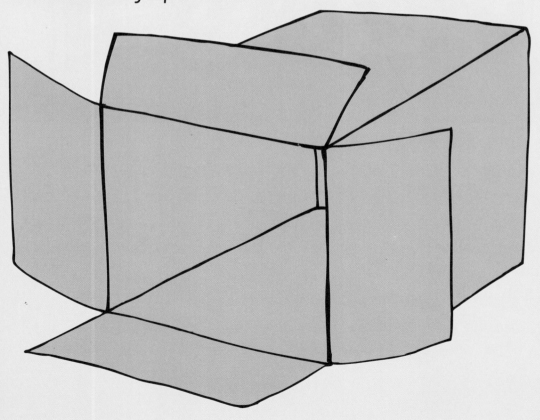

On the Beach

B1 and B2 are on beach patrol. Count how many times the objects at the bottom of the page appear in the picture.
Write the number in each box.

35 The answers are on page 61.

Match Up

Draw lines linking each of the Teddies to the things that belong to them.

pink bows

tutu

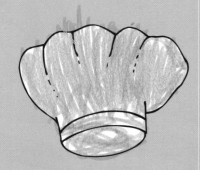

chef's hat

The answers are on page 61.

Yellow

B1 and B2 are playing a trick on you. What things in this picture should really be yellow? Put a tick in the boxes.

| ○ sun | ☐ | ○ sunflower | ☐ | ○ cloud | ☐ |
| ○ chicks | ☐ | ○ sand | ☐ | ○ grass | ☐ |

The answers are on page 61.

It's Tuesday

Read the story in words and pictures.

"Are you thinking what I'm thinking  ?"

"I think I am  ." "It's Tuesday and time

to chase the Teddies!" B2 looked through the

 and saw  and  playing

on the beach. The Bananas in Pyjamas ran out

of the 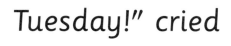 . The Teddies looked up. "It's

Tuesday!" cried  . They dropped their

 and ran away and hid behind a  .

38

The Bananas could not find them! "Oh well,"

said  . "We'll have to try again next

Tuesday!" The Bananas went back to their

 .  and  crept out. They

found their , which were full of  .

But just as they were about to go through

their front 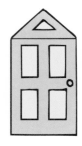 and jumped

out from behind a  . "Caught you!"

they cried.

Leaves

Lulu and Amy are collecting leaves. Can you help them sort the leaves into pairs? Draw lines to join the leaves that are the same.

Banana Maze

B1 and B2 are playing hide-and-seek with the Teddies.
Can you help the Teddies find the Bananas?

Start

Finish

41

Birthday Party Time!

One day B1 and B2 were feeling very sad. "Are you thinking what I'm thinking, B1?"

"I think I am, B2."

"We need something to cheer us up."

Just then there was a knock on the door. It was Lulu. "Hello, Bananas," she said. "We're waiting for you to chase us. It's Tuesday!"

"We know," said the Bananas. "But we don't feel very happy today. We feel too sad to chase you."

"That's awful!" said Lulu. "You need cheering up. Shall I make you something to eat?"

The Bananas shook their heads. They didn't feel like eating.

"Shall I show you my new dance?" asked Lulu.

The Bananas shook their heads again. No, that wouldn't cheer them up.

Lulu was running out of ideas. "What is the one thing that would cheer you up?"

"Are you thinking what I'm thinking, B2?"

"I think I am, B1."

"The one thing that will cheer us up is a birthday party."

Lulu was puzzled. "But it's a long time until your birthdays," she said. "Lots and lots of sleeps before then."

"We know," said the Bananas.

Lulu decided to talk to Morgan and Amy. She went back home and told them all about the sad Bananas.

"A birthday party is the only thing that will cheer them up," said Lulu. "But today isn't the Bananas' birthday."

Amy had an idea. "Let's have a party for the Bananas anyway. We can PRETEND it's their birthday."

"Yes," said Morgan. "Why not? It will be fun!"

"Let's get to work then," said Lulu. "I'll blow up lots of balloons and make some paper chains."

"I'll make a pretend birthday cake and some yellow jelly," said Morgan.

"And I'll make pretend birthday cards and wrap up a big pretend present," said Amy.

Soon everything was ready and the Teddies went round to the Bananas' house. When B1 and B2 opened the door the Teddies started to sing. "Happy Pretend Birthday To You," they sang.

The Bananas were very surprised! "Are you thinking what I'm thinking, B2?"

"I think I am, B1."

"It's Pretend Birthday Party Time!"

They all went round to the Teddies' house. There were blue and yellow balloons everywhere! There were paper chains, too, and a big pretend birthday cake and lots of yellow jelly on the table.

Amy gave the Bananas their pretend birthday cards and their pretend present wrapped in a big blue and white box.

"Are you thinking what I'm thinking, B2?"

"I think I am, B1."

"This pretend birthday party has cheered us up Teddies. Thank you," said the Bananas in Pyjamas. "We don't feel sad any more!"

45

Paper Chains

"I'll show you how to make PAPER CHAINS like the ones I made for the Bananas' pretend birthday party."

You will need:

coloured paper

sticky tape

safety scissors

1. Ask a grown-up to help you cut lots of strips of paper about 12cm long and 3cm wide.

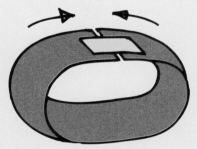

2. Make one strip into a circle. Join the ends with a little piece of sticky tape.

3. Put the next strip THROUGH the first one. Make it into a circle and join the ends with tape. Carry on like this until the chain is as long as you want it.

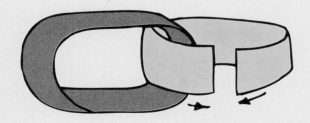

Birthday Cards

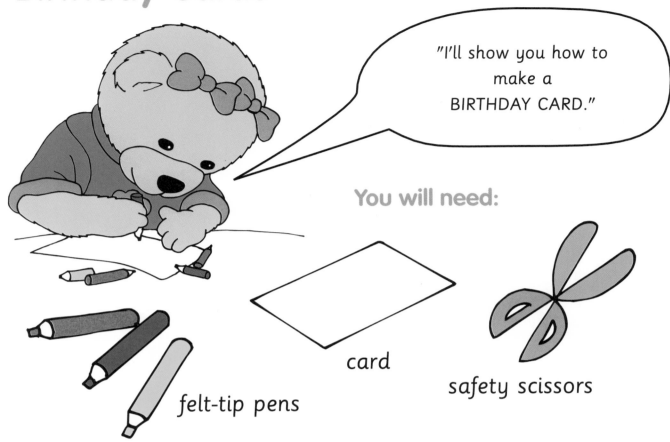

"I'll show you how to make a BIRTHDAY CARD."

You will need:

card

safety scissors

felt-tip pens

1. Ask a grown-up to help you cut out a piece of card. It should be about 30cm long and 20cm high.

2. Fold the card in half along the long side. Now you have a card 15cm wide and 20cm high.

3. Keep the fold on the left side. Use felt-tip pens to draw a picture on the front of the card. Write your message inside.

Morgan's Surprise

Morgan was very busy. He had collected lots of things. There was a big cardboard box, empty yogurt pots and some egg boxes. "What's all this old rubbish for?" asked Lulu. "This isn't old rubbish," said Morgan. "What is it then?" asked Lulu. "A surprise!" said Morgan.

Morgan got to work. He stuck yogurt pots on the outside of the box. He cut out some egg box cups and stuck them on too. Amy walked round the box. "What are you making, Morgan?" she asked. "Is it a car?" Morgan shook his head. "No," he said. "I can't tell you. It will spoil the surprise."

Morgan removed the flaps from the top of the box then he cut out some circles and stuck them inside the box. He glued on some plastic bottle tops, too. "Now all I need are these two long pieces of cardboard," he said. Amy was watching. "What is it?" she asked. "Wait and see," said Morgan.

"It's going to be a surprise. A BIG surprise!" Amy and Lulu weren't the only ones who were curious about Morgan's big box. The Bananas in Pyjamas watched him through the window.

Soon Morgan's surprise was finished. It was a plane! It had two wings and lots of dials and knobs inside. Morgan was the pilot. He even had a pilot's hat to wear. His passengers all thought their trip was great fun!

Banana Jokes

The Bananas in Pyjamas love telling jokes. Here are some about bananas!

Why did the banana split?
Because it saw the apple turnover!

What does a banana call his grandmother?
Ba-Nana.

How did the banana get out of the tree?
He did a bun-chie jump!

Why did the banana have so many friends?
He had a-peel!

How did the banana get away from the police?
He gave them the slip!

What is yellow with red spots?
A banana with measles.

What happened when the banana got sunburnt?
It peeled.

Munchy Maze

Yummy! Munchy Honey Cakes! But which path will lead the Teddies to them, 1, 2 or 3?

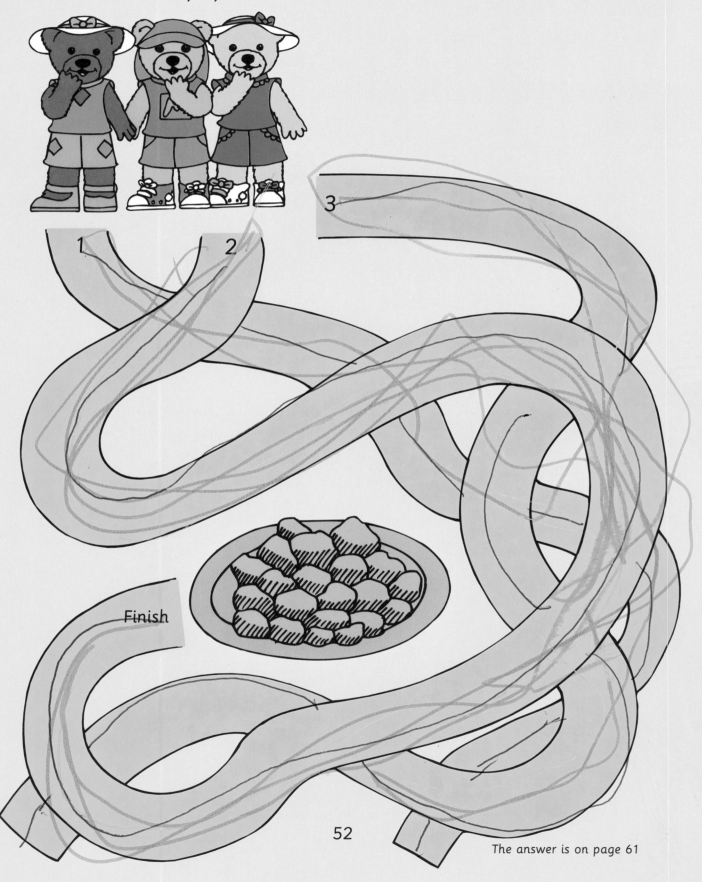

Finish

52

The answer is on page 61

Rat in a Hat's Shop

These two pictures of Rat in a Hat's shop look the same. But 5 things are different in the bottom picture. Can you find the 5 differences? Draw a ring around each one.

The answers are on page 61.

Footprints!

One morning the Bananas in Pyjamas were on beach patrol. B1 picked up litter and put it into a big bin. Then they both went to the water's edge.

The sand was wet. B1 looked behind him. "Look at my footprints in the wet sand, B2. Look how big they are!"

B2 jumped up and down. His shoes left deep footprints in the wet sand. The Bananas in Pyjamas had fun making shapes in the sand. When they turned their feet this way and that the shapes didn't look like their footprints at all.

"Are you thinking what I'm thinking, B2?"

"I think I am, B1. It's Trick Time!"

The Bananas in Pyjamas were busy all morning using their shoes to make big shapes in the wet sand. When they had finished they went off to find the Teddies. The Teddies were at Rat in a Hat's shop.

"Come quickly!" said B1 to the Teddies.

"Come to the beach!" said B2. "There are footprints in the sand!"

"What is so unusual about that?" asked Morgan.

"These are not ordinary footprints," said B1. "They are BIG ones!"

"HUGE ones!" said B2. He held his arms wide apart. "About as big as this!"

The Teddies followed the Bananas to the beach. Rat in a Hat went with them. B1 pointed to a footprint in the sand. Lulu gasped. It was very big!

"What could have made a footprint like that?" said Morgan. "A sea monster?"

Amy looked all around. "Could it be a dinosaur?"

"Or a big wild animal!" said Lulu.

"The footprints go over there," said B1.

"Yes," said B2. "They lead into the bushes."

"We must follow them," said Lulu. "We must find out what made these footprints."

They didn't notice that B1 and B2 had slipped away.

Lulu stopped at the bushes. She took a deep breath. "Follow me," she said.

Amy and Morgan walked behind her, holding hands. Rat in a Hat came next. He kept looking back, just in case anything was following him.

Lulu looked at the last footprint. "Hello!" she called in a little voice. "Is anyone here?"

"Grrr!" came the reply.

The Teddies jumped right into the air. The bushes shook and out leapt the Bananas in Pyjamas!

"You trickers!" said Morgan.

"Yes, we made those big footprint shapes!" said the Bananas.

The Teddies and Rat in a Hat laughed. They all had lots of fun making more shapes in the sand until the waves came up and washed them all away...

Pyjamas

"The Bananas have striped pyjamas. What would you like on YOUR pyjamas? Use crayons or coloured pencils to draw a pattern on these pyjamas."

Flying Kites

The Bananas and the Teddies are flying kites in the park. Can you sort out the tangle of strings?

1. Who has the blue kite? 2. What colour is the Bananas' kite?
3. Whose kite has blown away? 4. Whose kite is a triangle shape?

The answers are on page 61

Answers to Puzzles

pages 6 and 7 Welcome to Cuddles Avenue

1. B1 and B2
2. She is at the door of her house
3. Morgan
4. Amy

page 18 Lulu's Puzzle

page 19 Amy's Alphabet

House, **T**able, h**A**t, **B**alloon, **C**ake.

page 26 I Spy...

Bat, ball, bicycle, basket, book, bird, box, button, bell and bucket.

page 29 Hide-and-Seek

B1 is behind the tree.
B2 is under the towel.

page 35 On the Beach

There are 2 boats, 4 clouds, 5 shells, 3 birds, 1 umbrella and 2 towels.

page 36 Match up

Morgan and his chef's hat;
Lulu and her ballet tutu;
Amy and her bows.

page 37 Yellow

The sun, chicks, sand and sunflower should be yellow.

page 52 Munchy Maze

Path 2 leads to the Munchy Honey Cakes.

page 41 Banana Maze

page 53 Rat in a Hat's Shop

page 60 Flying Kites

1. Morgan
2. Yellow
3. Amy's
4. Lulu's